ALIVE!
TO TELL
THE
STORY

A RESURRECTION MUSICAL

SUSIE HARE

Kevin
Mayhew

We hope you enjoy *Alive! . . . to tell the story*. Further copies are available from your local Kevin Mayhew stockist.

In case of difficulty, please contact the publisher direct by writing to:

The Sales Department
KEVIN MAYHEW LTD
Buxhall
Stowmarket
Suffolk
IP14 3BW

Phone 01449 737978
Fax 01449 737834
E-mail info@kevinmayhewltd.com

Please ask for our complete catalogue of outstanding Church Music.

Also available

Professional backing track CD (Catalogue No: 1490079)
Publicity pack (Catalogue No: 1900400)

First published in Great Britain in 2001 by Kevin Mayhew Ltd.

© Copyright 2001 Kevin Mayhew Ltd.

ISBN 1 84003 825 X
ISMN M 57004 963 9
Catalogue No: 1450238

0 1 2 3 4 5 6 7 8 9

Music Setter and Editor: Donald Thomson
Proof reader: Linda Ottewell

Cover design: Angela Selfe

Printed and bound in Great Britain

Foreword

Lazarus, whom Jesus raised from the dead and who is, quite literally, alive to tell the story, introduces this musical.

As we observe how Jesus' death and resurrection affected some of the people who witnessed them, we are challenged to consider the effect of these events on our own lives, two thousand years down the line.

With which of the characters do we most identify?

Is it the Chief Priests and Teachers of Law, who were so steeped in tradition and rules and regulations that they had become inflexible in their attitudes?

Is it Judas, who, although he was a follower of Jesus, was not strong enough to resist the wiles of Satan?

Is it Nicodemus, who needed to be born again before he could enter the Kingdom of Heaven?

Is it Peter, who loved Jesus, but, for fear of his own safety, denied that he even knew him?

Is it the centurion, who was too hardened by his job to change his lifestyle?

Is it Pilate, who chose expediency above principle?

Whichever character we identify with, this story can speak hope into our hearts. For, just as Lazarus was rescued from death, just as Jesus himself was raised, we too can be made alive in Christ – alive to tell others the story of the glorious hope of Easter.

Acknowledgements

I am extremely grateful to Andrew Redbond for his valued contribution to this work, to Ruth Evans for her wisdom and encouragement, and to Richard Lewis for all his help in producing the CD.

Production Notes

As with most productions, *Alive! . . . to tell the story* can be staged as lavishly as resources allow or as simply as they dictate. The general atmosphere of certain scenes will obviously be enhanced if sets are detailed but a minimalist stage is perfectly acceptable – and will probably be the approach for the majority of performances.

Full costume will add something to a performance that jeans and T-shirts will never create, but a simple prop (hat, cloak, sword, crown, etc.) will suffice to represent the character. It will also facilitate the interchange of characters more easily than frantic costume changing in the wings.

Not every venue will have sophisticated sound and lighting equipment but if you are fortunate in having some (and, most importantly, someone who knows what to do with it) use it imaginatively throughout. Technical rehearsals are not always given the priority they deserve, resulting in performance disasters that could have been averted.

The approximate duration of *Alive! . . . to tell the story* is 1 hour 35 minutes, but reduce or extend certain scenes if you wish. The following suggestions are by no means prescriptive and producers should feel free to be flexible in order to encompass the resources and talents at their disposal.

OVERTURE
This is a good way of settling the audience and introducing melodies. However, it is optional.

SCENE 1
Lazarus is an energetic, enthusiastic personality who keeps the balance between his two very different sisters – Martha, the homely, bustling type, and Mary, the quieter, more contemplative character. The sisters should be engaging in some actions behind the song and perhaps doing a step routine between verses.

SCENE 2
Those not brave enough to have Jesus riding a real donkey could have him being lifted aloft and well disguised by the crowds. Alternatively, the cheering crowds could be looking ahead, by implication following a donkey, which is never actually seen. Either way, take advantage of aisles, etc., and make this song as joyful as you can.

SCENE 3
Here we have a situation where priests are seemingly condoning the practice of money-lending by allowing it to take place in the temple (and probably getting a good pay-off for doing so). They are strutting about, looking important and there is much activity and noise. When Jesus and his disciples enter – possibly looking for somewhere to teach or to pray quietly – Jesus is firstly amazed by what he sees, then angry. For the benefit of those in the audience who might not be familiar with the Gospel narrative, the action here must be very clear.

SCENE 4
The events of the Passover Supper are mimed during the singing of the song 'Jesus said'. This will involve careful rehearsing to get the timing right.

SCENE 5

Here again the narration of Lazarus throughout the scene will need careful rehearsal to get the timing right. If you have someone who can contribute some creative dance, then an angel (or a group of them) – taking strength from God, giving strength to Jesus and lifting his spirit up – would certainly be of benefit here.

SCENE 6

'Barbarous Barabbas' must express the determination and anger of the crowd. It is fairly challenging to sing in places but it will be worth the effort for the resulting impact.

SCENE 7

As an alternative to Jesus being hoisted on a cross, mime is sufficient – and certainly safer. 'I was there' will need carefully thought out, imaginative movement if this song is to have maximum visual as well as musical impact.

The priests who mock Jesus around the foot of the cross ('If you are the Son of God') should be as menacing as possible. A dance routine would be beneficial here. 'Today you shall be with me' is a simple song, preceding total silence and darkness. Then comes the thunderstorm and the rending of the temple curtain, which needs to be well rehearsed and on cue.

SCENE 8

This shows us two men, both respected members of the Sanhedrin, who are posing questions that might be in the minds of some of the audience. There is a general feeling of having let Jesus down, followed by a realisation that what Jesus told Nicodemus is now making more sense.

SCENE 9

Mary's utter devotion to Jesus and her gratitude for all he has done for her is reflected in this song.

SCENE 10

There is a general air of despair here. The disciples have been left without a leader and – or so it seems to them – without a purpose in life any more. They are dazed, confused and worried and the last thing they need is a hysterical woman in their midst. Their disbelief is turned to joy in 'Alive!' and this song needs some vigorous, imaginative choreography. There are few things less easy on the eye than a stage full of people just jigging about with no real structure to their dancing. Make this an opportunity to have a good party on stage – maybe doing a line-dance to a repeat, instrumental of the song.

It might seem out of character for a sober and upright member of the Sanhedrin to suddenly launch into a calypso; but here is a man who has been born again and wants to let his hair down! Everyone should enter into the spirit of things with 'If you want to follow Jesus'. Again, make use of any choreography talent you may have in your team.

In sheer jubilation Lazarus is unable to resist another rendering of 'Today I am alive', before he delivers the very core of the show's message.

The finale should be a triumphant expression of joy and hope, culminating in 'One day we shall be with him', which, as it were, stands outside the chronology of events, bringing a post-resurrection interpretation to what has happened.

Cast

SOLOISTS
Lazarus
Mary Magdalene
Peter
Centurion
Mary, mother of James
Nicodemus
Pilate
Judas Iscariot

GROUP SINGERS
Mary
Martha
Chief Priests (4)
Teachers of Law (3)
Quartet (Passover Supper and Calvary)
Mary, mother of James

DANCERS
Angels at the Mount of Olives

NON-SINGING/NON-SPEAKING PARTS
Jesus
Two thieves on crosses at Calvary
More soldiers
More Chief Priests
More Teachers of Law

OTHERS
Servant girls in courtyard (2)
Men in courtyard (2)
Herod
Herod's soldiers (2)
Passer-by at Calvary
Joseph of Arimathea
Malchus, a servant
Moneylenders in temple
Andrew
Philip
Matthew
John
Judas, son of James
Simon
Bartholomew
James, son of Alpheus
James

PEOPLE IN CROWDS
Scene 2 (Entry into Jerusalem)
Scene 3 (In the temple)
Scene 5 (The Mount of Olives)
Scene 6 (Before Pilate)
Scene 7 (Calvary)
Scene 10 (Resurrection Morning)

Songs and Incidental Music

APPROXIMATE TOTAL DURATION: 1 HOUR 35 MINUTES

ALIVE! . . . TO TELL THE STORY

Words and Music: Susie Hare

OVERTURE

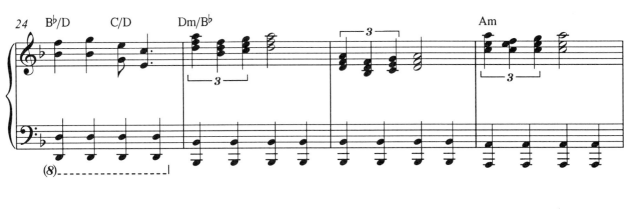

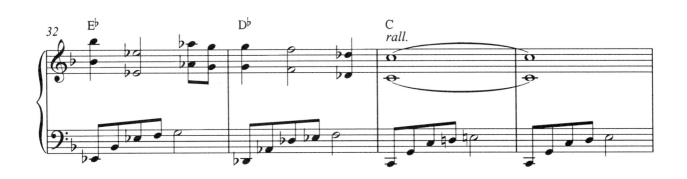

Gently and a little slower

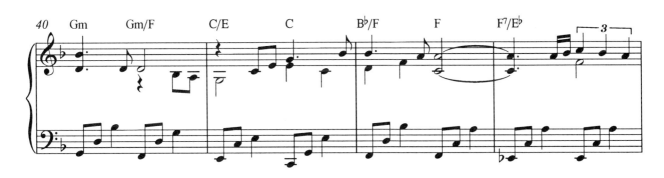

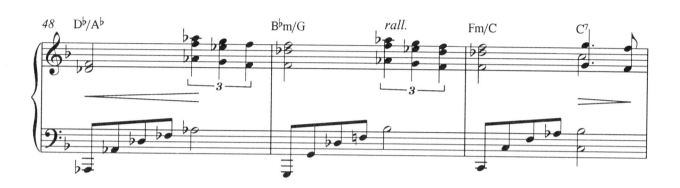

Tempo I

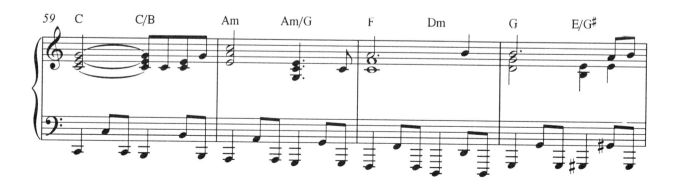

SCENE 1: THE HOME OF LAZARUS, MARY AND MARTHA

Lazarus, Mary and Martha, having just finished a meal together.

Lazarus	*(patting his stomach)* Gosh, Martha, that was one of the best meals I've had in my life!
Martha	Talking of your life, our Lazarus, you just remember how lucky you are to have it. I'm not convinced you're not overdoing things.
Lazarus	*(sighs)* Dear sister – for the umpteenth time – I'm fine.
Martha	Well, you're looking a bit peaky.
Lazarus	*(mimicking)* Well, you're looking a bit peaky.
Martha	I was only asking!
Lazarus	*(slightly regretting his lack of appreciation)* Sorry, Martha; thanks for your concern – but I've never felt better actually.
Mary	She's right, though, Laz; you are looking quite tired. You haven't been at all well.
Martha	Now that has to be the understatement of the year.
Mary	Well, not long ago he was at death's door.
Martha	*(laughs)* He was a little bit more than at death's door. He went right on in, sat down and put his feet up. He does look better than when he came out of the tomb, though.
Lazarus	And a darned sight better than when I went in! *(he and Martha laugh)*
Mary	I don't think death is something to laugh about. Jesus wept over you, Lazarus.
Lazarus	*(more soberly)* Yes, I – I heard he did.
Mary	When it all happened, we knew Jesus was only a couple of miles away, and obviously we sent for him immediately. But he stayed in Jerusalem for two more days and we couldn't understand that. Knowing how fond of you he is . . . well, we did think he'd come rather more quickly.
Martha	Must have had his reasons.
Lazarus	*(chuckling)* Martha, Jesus always has his reasons, believe you me.
Martha	I went up the road to wait for him and when he did eventually arrive, well . . . I'm ashamed to say I ticked him off a bit for being too late. I'm horrified now to think I had the cheek. We had hoped he could have healed you, but by then you'd been in the tomb for four days.
Lazarus	But, Martha, you should have known that God would give Jesus whatever he asks.

Martha	That's just what Jesus said. He said 'I am the resurrection and the life. He who believes in me will live, even though he dies.'
Lazarus	Well, there you go then. He was absolutely right, wasn't he? 'Cos here I am – and I feel more alive since I was dead . . . than I did before I died . . . when . . . I was alive. *(confuses even himself)* Er . . . if you see what I mean. I think what I'm trying to say is that it's possible to think you're alive when, actually, you're just . . . well . . . just existing.
Mary	But what's it *like* – being dead?
Lazarus	I wish I could explain but death does rather play havoc with your memory. All I know is that I'm *so* thankful to be alive. I can't keep still, I can't keep quiet . . .
Martha	*(interrupting, rather sarcastically)* Huh, *tell* us about it!
Lazarus	Okay then – I will!

TODAY I AM ALIVE TO TELL THE STORY

24 C   C/B♭   A7   D7

peo - ple, still   they said: 'Did - n't you know?

27 Dm7/G   C   F   G   Cdim/G   G9

He is al - rea - dy dead.'   The

30 C6   B♭   A

vil - la - gers were look - ing out for Je - sus.   They
Je - sus came to find where I was ly - ing,   it

32 D7   D7/A   D

saw him com - ing through   our gate.   They
must have been quite plain   to see;   I

go back to bed;

did-n't you know?

You're sup-posed to be dead!'

Mary and Martha exit with dishes and Lazarus stands alone, talking to audience.

Lazarus   Yes, today I *am* alive to tell the story; but before you misunderstand me, it's not *my* story I want to tell. Oh, mine is miraculous enough. In fact it's amazing. But it's nothing compared to his. They're saying *his* story will change the world. Jesus, my friend. The one who gave me back my life . . . and then lost his own.

We didn't know it was going to be like it was. Okay, so we should have, he told us often enough, didn't he – 'The son of man must suffer much . . .' – but the whole prospect seemed unbelievable. I mean he was – *is* – so powerful. He can do anything. Heal the sick with a touch. No – not even a touch – he just spoke to them. A blind man sees, a deaf man hears, a cripple walks and even the dead are raised. *(chuckles)* I'm living proof of that!

He was a walking contradiction really. Such humility, yet, at the same time, such unbelievable power. There seemed to be no end to what he was capable of. We thought it was only a matter of time before the glorious revolution and we had wild dreams about what Jesus could achieve. We knew he could achieve anything. *(pause)* We just hadn't planned on it happening this way. Even our wildest dreams weren't this wild.

The King of kings – crucified by the very people he came to save. Ironic. But the thing is – there are none so blind as those who will not see; none so deaf as those who will not hear – and that was them. *(pause)* Is it *you?*

Let's go back a bit – so that you can see and hear for yourselves.

Introduction to song starts. People enter, shouting and waving palm branches, etc.

19

SCENE 2: THE ENTRY INTO JERUSALEM

HOSANNA

Brightly

Crowds begin to enter, waving palm branches, shouting etc.

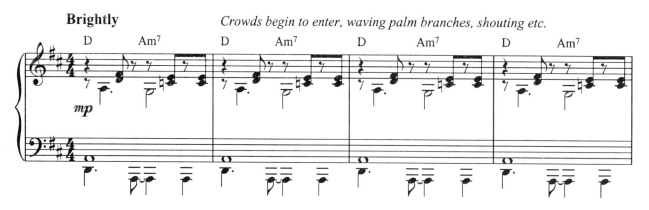

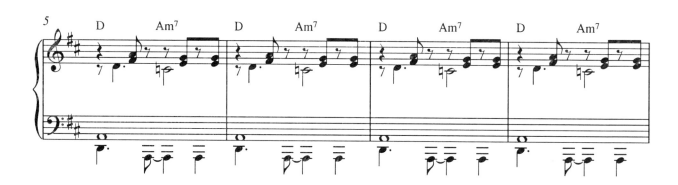

Lazarus *(shouting above the noise)* Jesus was riding into Jerusalem on a donkey and – as you can already hear – we were giving him a right royal welcome! *(he goes to join crowd)*

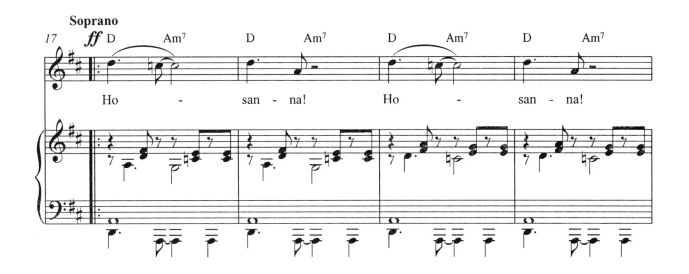

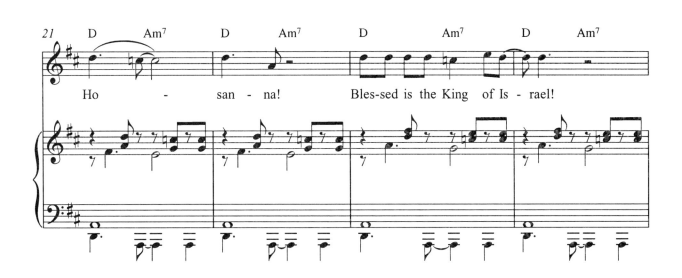

Sopranos and Tenors

Bles-sed is he who comes in the name of the Lord.

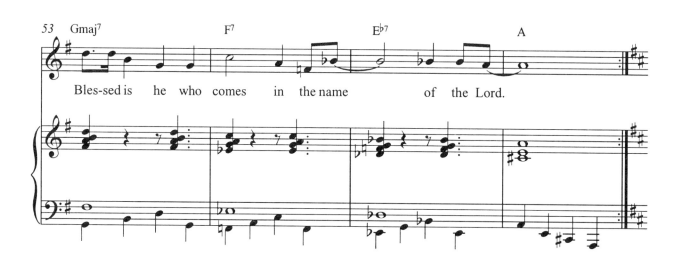

Bles-sed is he who comes in the name of the Lord.

(Crowd cheering, dancing etc.)

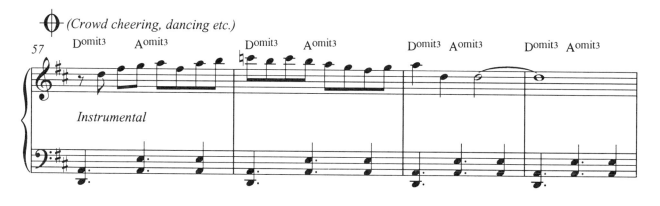

Instrumental

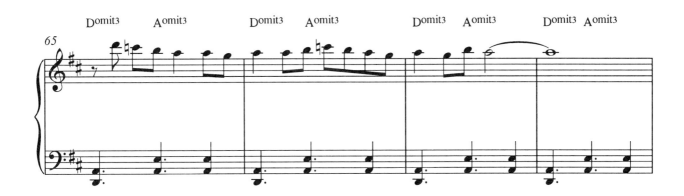

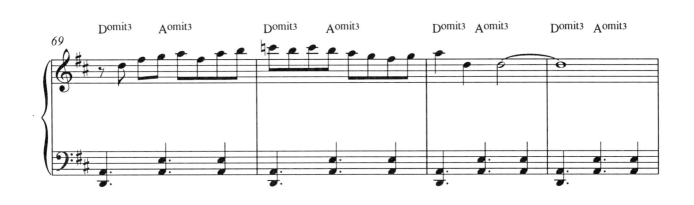

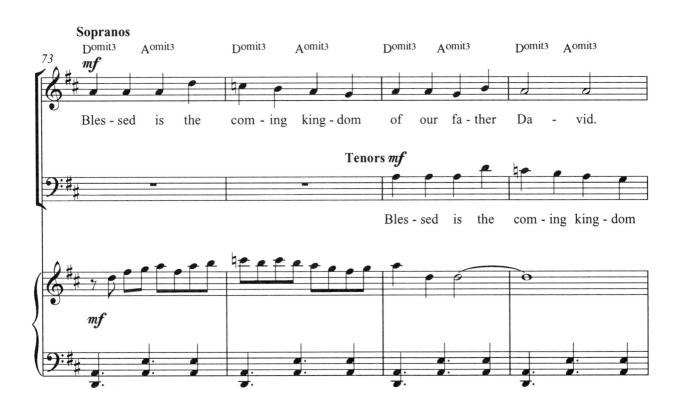

Bles - sed is the com - ing king - dom of our fa - ther Da - vid.

Bles - sed is the com - ing king - dom

Bles-sed is the King of Is - rael! Bles-sed is the King of Is-

- rael! Bles-sed is the King of Is - rael!

INCIDENTAL MUSIC 1

Crowds exit, all but Lazarus, Mary and Martha

Lazarus	Hey, wasn't that great. Cheering Jesus into the city. I think I've cheered myself hoarse. Or is it 'donkey'? *(nudges Mary and laughs)*
Martha	Probably more like 'ass' actually. *(pointedly looking at Lazarus)*
Mary	The thing is, though – I've been thinking – what's going to happen now?
Martha	We're going home to cook supper; that's what's going to happen now.
Mary	No, I mean now that Jesus has gone into Jerusalem – what next?
Lazarus	Something great, that's what. I can feel it. Something great is going to happen.
Mary	Yes, but those Pharisees – they don't like it.
Lazarus	That might be so, but they're powerless against him, aren't they?
Martha	No, Mary's right; those leaders – and the Saducees – you can see it in their eyes. They hate him. I'm really worried.
Lazarus	Look, I was dead and now I'm alive. Feel that. *(holds out his arm)* That was dead flesh. No, more importantly, feel here; *(touches his heart)* that's where I was dead. At heart. Peter's right, Jesus does have the words of eternal life. He *is* the one.
Mary	Well, why does he keep talking about suffering and dying then? *(the question stops everyone for a moment)*
Martha	Well . . . well, I guess he does suffer. The evil, the opposition, the Pharisees. But he's going to end all that, you wait and see.
Mary	I don't know. I have a feeling it's not that easy. I mean, Lazarus had to be dead before he was alive.
Lazarus	Come on, you two, everything's going to be fine. *(playfully slaps Martha on the back)* Now, when's supper, sister?
Martha	When someone gives me a hand with it, that's when.
Mary	Honestly, Martha, when will you ever learn that some things are more important than supper?
Lazarus	Probably never, Mary, but right now supper sounds a good idea to me. I'm dead hungry. *(Martha groans)* Oops, sorry!
Martha	Oh, go on with you! *(Martha ushers him out; Mary holds back for a moment)*
Mary	*(to herself)* What was that quote? 'I will strike the shepherd and the sheep will be scattered'. I don't like it. I don't like it at all. *(she follows them out)*

SCENE 3: IN THE TEMPLE

INCIDENTAL MUSIC 2

Moderato

In temple – money lenders trading – condsiderable activity and noise

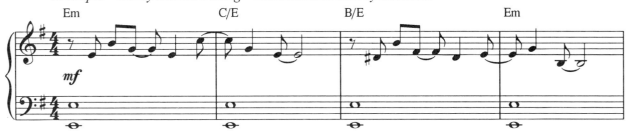

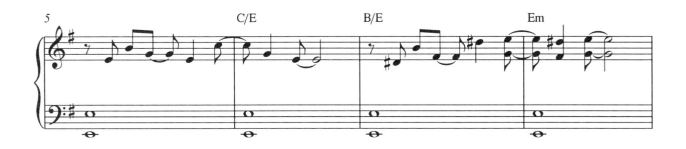

Priests and Teachers enter – generally organising

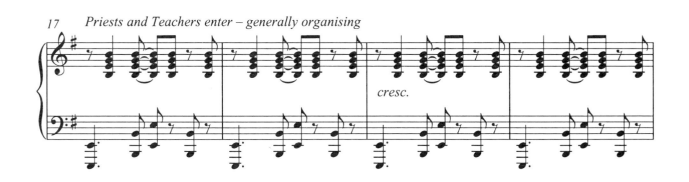

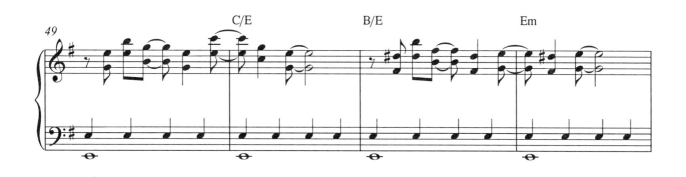

Jesus overturns tables of money lenders

Crowd looks amazed – Priests and Teachers look angry

Jesus and disciples leave temple

1st Chief Priest	We shouldn't have to tolerate this man. Who gives him the right to do these things?
2nd C.P.	We asked him that once if you remember and he refused to tell us.
3rd C.P.	Yes, he did his usual thing: answered the question by asking another question. 'Tell me', he said, 'Did John's right to baptize come from God or from man?' We were trapped because we knew whichever we said, we'd be in trouble. He just seems to have a way that is completely confounding.
1st Teacher of Law	*And* totally unacceptable. He's undermining our teaching, that's for sure. The worrying thing is, the people seem to think he's wonderful. They'll follow him anywhere. They'll sit and listen to him for hours. It's crazy!
1st C.P.	I fail to see how people can put their faith in someone who just . . . just pitches up and starts pontificating on everything under the sun – moon and stars included – when we're the ones who have the knowledge of the law and the recognised authority to expound it.
2nd C.P.	The confusing thing is, though, he seems to have the ability to explain the law – without having had the kind of training *we've* had. It's almost as if he was . . . well . . . born with it.
1st T.O.L	I hate to say this, but one does have to envy his talent for getting on the people's level; it wins them round every time.
4th C.P.	And raising that Lazarus from the dead was a major drawback for us – Jesus' following took a rapid upturn. If only we'd succeeded in our plans to kill Lazarus, we might have wiped the smile off a few faces.
2nd T.O.L	If we let him carry on like this everyone will believe in him and destroy our temple and our nation.
3rd T.O.L	But remember what Caiaphas said – better to get rid of one man than have a whole nation perishing.
2nd T.O.L	What are you saying, exactly?
3rd T.O.L	I'm saying there are no two ways about it: this Jesus has to go!

(Straight into the next song on the cue 'this Jesus has to go!')

WE WANT TO KNOW

Al - though this kind of thing has not been done be - fore,

your of - fer is the sort we can't re - fuse; and it would seem that

now the days are num - bered for the one who says he is King of the

Jews.

They exit, looking gleeful at the forthcoming prospect

SCENE 4: IN THE UPPER ROOM

JESUS SAID: 'TAKE THIS BREAD'

Jesus and his disciples are reclining at a table
Quartet to side front stage
Events of Passover Supper are mimed during song

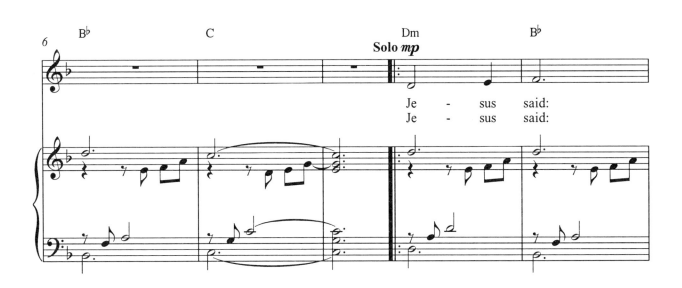

Je - sus said:
Je - sus said:

'Take this bread, it is my bo -
'Take this wine, it is my blood;

re - mem - ber me.
re - mem - ber me.

Then Je - sus said: 'One of you will be - tray me.' They all start - ed ask - ing, 'Is it

I?'

41

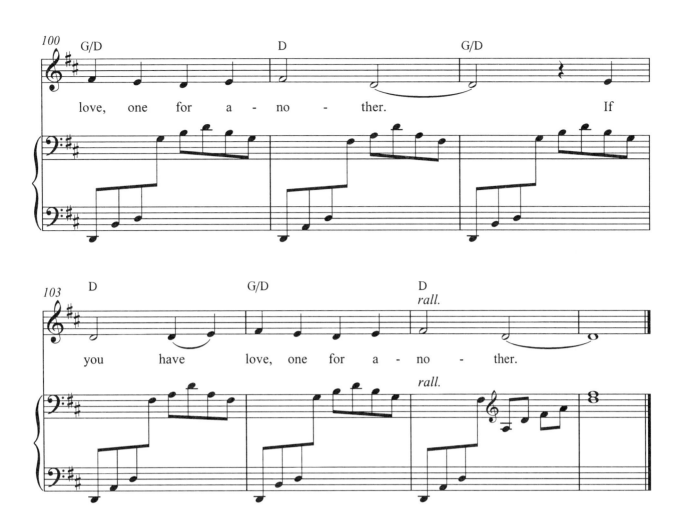

SCENE 5: THE MOUNT OF OLIVES

Lazarus comes to side of stage to narrate as the events of the Mount of Olives are mimed.

Lazarus   Then Jesus went with his disciples to a place called The Mount of Olives. Taking Peter, James and John with him, he said to the others: 'Sit here while I pray. My soul is overwhelmed with sorrow to the point of death. Stay here and keep watch.' He went a little way ahead of them, knelt down and started to pray: 'My father, if it is possible, may this cup be taken from me; yet not as I will but as you will.' An angel from heaven appeared and strengthened him whilst he prayed.

Then he returned to his disciples and found them sleeping. 'Could you not watch with me for one hour?' he asked. 'Watch and pray so that you will not fall into temptation. The spirit is willing but the body is weak.' He went away a second time and prayed. This time he said: 'My father, if it is not possible for this cup to be taken away unless I drink it may your will be done.'

When he came back, he again found his disciples sleeping because their eyes were heavy. So he left them and went away once more. He prayed for the third time, saying the same thing.

When he returned to the disciples he said to them: 'Are you still sleeping and resting? Look, the hour is near and the Son of Man is betrayed into the hands of sinners. Rise, let us go; here comes my betrayer.'

As the people approached Jesus, Judas stepped out from the crowd. Going at once to Jesus, he said: 'Rabbi' and kissed him.

The soldiers seized Jesus and arrested him and with that Peter drew his sword and cut off the right ear of Malchus, the High Priest's servant. But Jesus said: 'No more of this!' He touched the man's ear and healed him.

Then, seizing Jesus, they led him away and took him to the High Priest's house.

INCIDENTAL MUSIC 3

47

Angel withdraws to side

Then he returned to his disciples . . .

49

When he returned . . .

. . . here comes my betrayer.'

As the people approached Jesus . . .

51

... the High Priest's servant.

Peter cuts off ear

But Jesus said ...

... and healed him.

Then, seizing Jesus ...

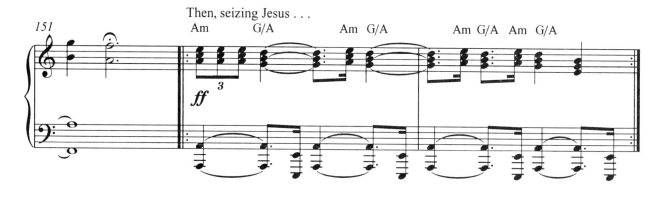

... the High Priest's house.

As Jesus is led away, Peter follows at a distance
but other disciples run off in opposite direction

Jesus has been taken to the corner of the courtyard where his captors are speaking to him (not heard). They have their backs to the main proceedings. Peter joins a group sitting by a fire. He looks uneasy. To help ease his conscience he has followed Jesus, but 'from afar' and now tries to associate himself with the servants. He sits down with a group by the fire and pretends to be one of them.

1st Servant-Girl	*(standing away from the fire with another small group, looking wistfully at Peter)* See that man over there? I'm sure he was with him.
1st Man	*(yawning)* With whom?
1st S.G.	With *him* . . . Jesus . . . I'm sure he was.
1st Man	*(still seeming bored)* Only one way to find out.
1st S.G.	Shall we ask him?
1st Man	We? You're the one who wants to know; ask him yourself.

1st Servant-Girl looks pleadingly at the man.

1st Man	Go on!
1st S.G.	*(coming up to Peter)* Weren't you one of the people with Jesus of Galilee?
Peter	Who? I don't know what you're talking about.
1st Man	*(coming up to fire)* Looks like you were wrong then.

1st Servant-Girl looks rather forlorn and goes to join group. They converse quietly.

2nd S.G.	*(after a long stare at Peter, turns to the others)* It *was* him, I'm sure of it.
Peter	*(standing up)* Listen, I've told you – I don't know the man.

The group look at Peter and discuss amongst themselves. One of them comes up to him.

2nd Man	Look here; we're sure it was you – and anyway, your accent gives it away. We know you're a Galilean. *(turning to others)* This fellow is definitely one of them.
Peter	*(more angered)* I do not know this man you're talking about.
2nd Man	*(holding up his hands, palms outwards and backing away)* Okay, okay.

The group of people leave, muttering amongst themselves that Peter is a liar, they were sure they'd seen him, etc. As they leave, the cock crows and Jesus turns around and looks at Peter – a chiding, yet compassionate look. Lights down on Jesus and his captors. Spotlight on Peter who walks to the front of stage, breaks down and cries, kneeling.

YOU SAID TO US

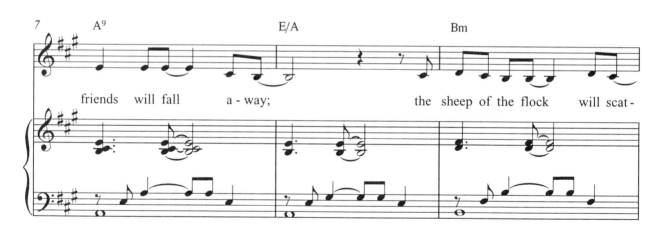

55

SCENE 6: JESUS BEFORE PILATE

Chief Priests and Elders are gathered together. General discussion which then subsides as Jesus is brought in before Pilate.

1st Teacher of Law	Sir – we have found this man subverting our nation. He opposes taxes to Caesar and *(sarcastically)* claims to be Christ – a king.
Pilate	Are you the King of the Jews?

Jesus gestures.

2nd T.O.L.	*(mocking)* King of the Jews? Look at him. Does he look like a king?
1st Chief Priest	He claims to be one, but then he claims to be a lot of things. All he does is go round misleading our people and setting them against us. That story he concocted the other day about the man who planted a vineyard was a deliberate snipe.
2nd C.P.	Yes, before the arrival of this . . . this *(sarcastically)* so-called king, we were popular with the people and they respected our teaching. *We* were the authority on God and then along he comes and starts talking as if he knows him personally!
3rd C.P.	He criticises our laws. He causes riots. He's nothing but a troublemaker!

Everyone together starts shouting out accusations, waving fists, etc.

Pilate	*(lifts his hands to silence the crowd)* Jesus, do you hear all of these things that you are accused of?

Jesus remains silent.

3rd T.O.L.	Huh! What kind of king is it that can't even speak up for himself?
4th C.P.	We have no king but Caesar – and you are no friend of Caesar's if you let this man go.
Pilate	But exactly what crime has he committed? I find no basis for a charge against him.
1st T.O.L.	He stirs up the people all over Judea by his teaching. He started in Galilee and has come all the way here.
Pilate	Is this man a Galilean then?
2nd T.O.L.	He is.
Pilate	In that case, he is under Herod's jurisdiction. Herod is in Jerusalem at the moment. Take Jesus to him and let's see what he makes of all this.

Soldiers march Jesus off. Lights down on Pilate's courtroom and up on sub-stage and Herod and his soldiers.

Herod	Well, well, well, Jesus. *(rubbing his hands together)* This *is* a pleasant surprise. 'I've heard so much about you' as they say! I gather you've been putting Pilate in a bit of a dilemma. Perhaps you'd like to tell us all about it? *(waits for response)* No? Well then, perhaps you'd like a chance to respond to all the accusations against you. You don't *look* like a rioter, but then, looks might be deceptive because you don't look much like a king either. *(chuckles)* Are you, as indeed men say you are, guilty of stirring up sedition from Galilee throughout the whole country? *(waits)* I'll take that to be a 'no' then . . . another one.
1st Soldier	*(eagerly believing his idea would save the moment)* Why not ask him to perform a miracle, Sir – *(sarcastically)* since they seem to be something of a speciality?

Herod	Mm, that would certainly provide reasonable proof that he is who he says he is.
2nd Soldier	Yes, wonderful idea. Come on then, Jesus – *(sneering)* Son of God!

Jesus stands motionless.

Herod	*(with a wry grin, speaking to soldiers)* Obviously a bashful performer . . . Jesus, it really would help your case if you were to come up with at least a little something to support it, and a miracle would be very impressive – doesn't matter what, you choose. *(gives Jesus a patronising smile)*

Jesus continues to stand motionless and the crowd starts shouting accusations.

Herod	*(above the noise)* Can't you hear them, man? Have you nothing to say for yourself at all?

Jesus still says nothing. Soldiers laugh mockingly and dress him in an elegant robe. They exit, together with Jesus and Herod. More general discussion in Pilate's court, then Jesus is brought back in.

1st T.O.L.	Ah, here he is, back again, the little blasphemer – *(he spits and holds up his fists to Jesus)*
2nd T.O.L.	What did Herod have to say to him, that's what we want to know.
Pilate	You brought this man to me as one who was inciting the people to rebellion. I have examined him and can find no basis for your charges. As you can see, Herod has come to the same conclusion and has sent him back to us. Therefore, I propose to punish him and then let him go.
Chief Priests	*(very angered)* Away with this man! Crucify him – and release Barabbas! *(they gesture to persuade the crowd and they nod in agreement)*
Pilate	I find no fault in him at all.
Crowd	Crucify him! Crucify him! *(they continue shouting during introduction to song)*

BARBAROUS BARABBAS

2nd time Attacca
Incidental Music 4

Slower

Pilate *mf*

Look-ing at his life I think you'll find there was no sin.

In all ho-nes-ty I have to say that I find no fault in him.

INCIDENTAL MUSIC 4

Fairly fast *Soldiers come and put a scarlet robe on Jesus and a staff in his right hand*

Soldiers: *(mockingly)* Hail, King of the Jews!

Soldiers spit on Jesus,
take back the staff and hit him

They take off his robe and lead him away

The people follow, still shouting

(repeat ad lib. until stage is clear)

SCENE 7: CALVARY

I WAS THERE

Crowd is assembled. Jesus and the two thieves are brought in and 'nailed'
to the crosses. His is inscribed 'King of the Jews'.

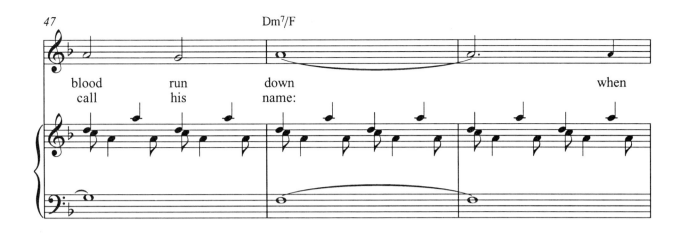

blood run down
call his name:
when

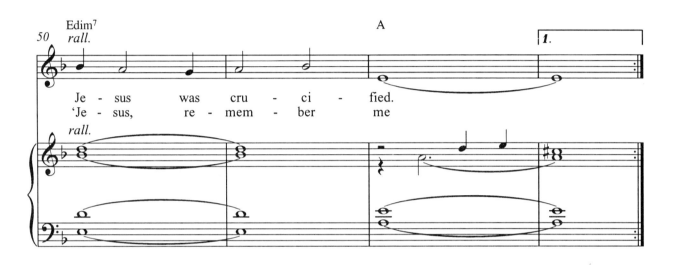

Je - sus was cru - ci - fied.
'Je - sus, re - mem - ber me

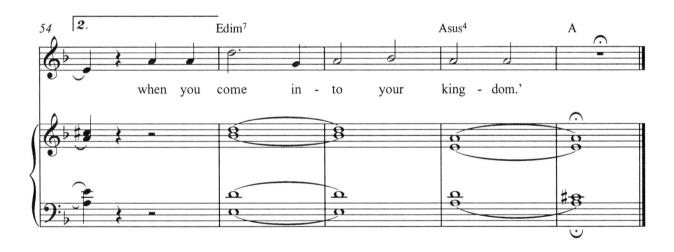

when you come in - to your king - dom.'

Passer-by   Hey! You who are going to destroy the temple and rebuild it in three days –
save yourself! Come down from the cross (*sarcastically*) if you *are* the Son of God.

IF YOU ARE THE SON OF GOD

You've saved o - thers in the past, so this need not be your last ho - ur.

Prove to us you have the pow - er!

Other mockers in crowd join in

If you are the Son of God, save your-self!

If you are the Son of God, save your-self!

TODAY YOU SHALL BE WITH ME IN PARADISE

Gently and unhurried

Jesus looks at the thief on the cross next to him

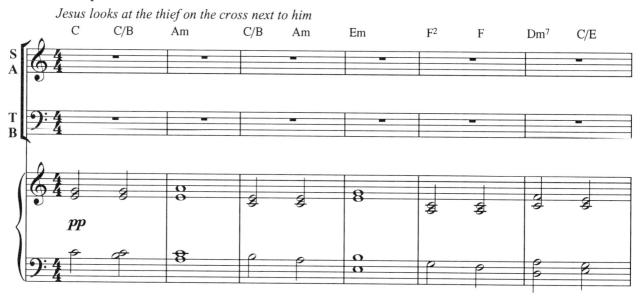

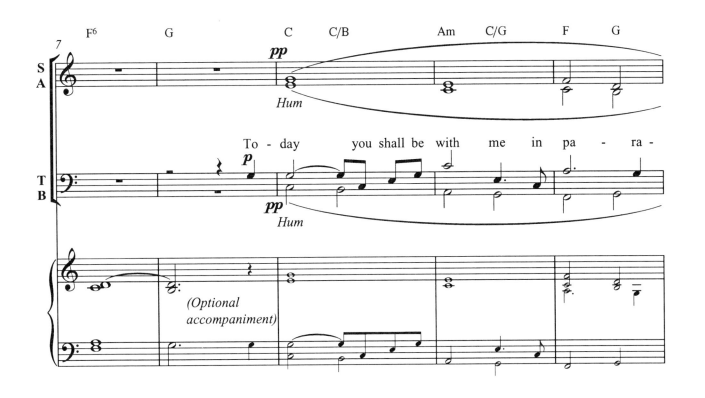

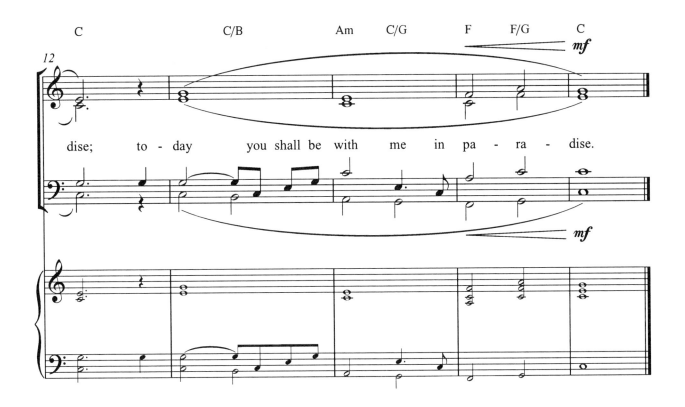

Jesus bows his head and dies

Complete darkness on stage and in auditorium

Sound effects: rending of temple curtain; thunderstorm

UNTIL TODAY

Pause. Spotlight on Centurion who comes to centre stage front

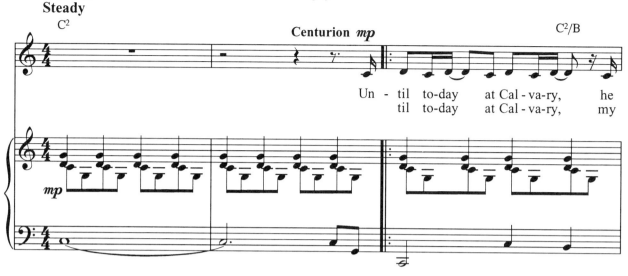

Un - til to-day at Cal - va-ry, he
til to-day at Cal - va-ry, my

did - n't mean a lot to me; I ne - ver thought a - bout him, I
stub-born heart pre - vent - ed me from e - ver real - ly know - ing the

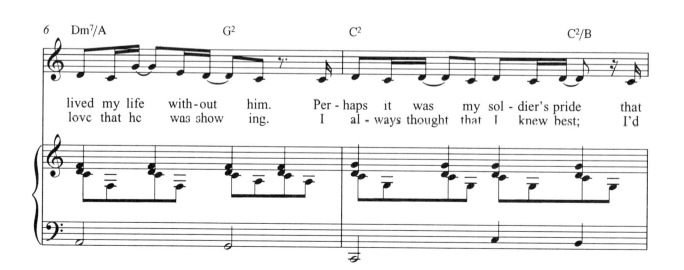

lived my life with-out him. Per - haps it was my sol - dier's pride that
love that he was show ing. I al - ways thought that I knew best; I'd

ne - ver knew for - give - ness till I saw it in his eyes; till I

heard him tell his fa - ther, 'They know not what they do.' Was it

me that he was mean - ing? Was it you?

Un - til to-day at Cal-va-ry, I did what was re-quired of me; it

Sure - ly this man was the Son of God, his

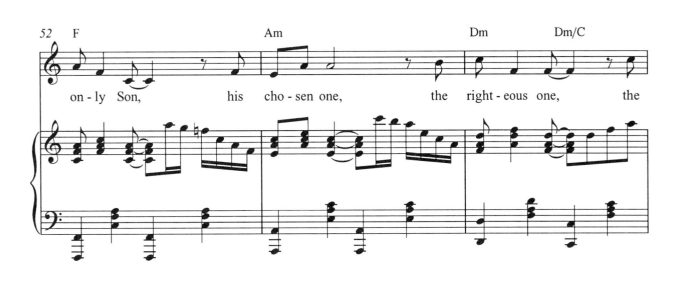

on - ly Son, his cho - sen one, the right - eous one, the

Lazarus steps forward to join Centurion

ho - ly one. Sure-ly this man was the Son of

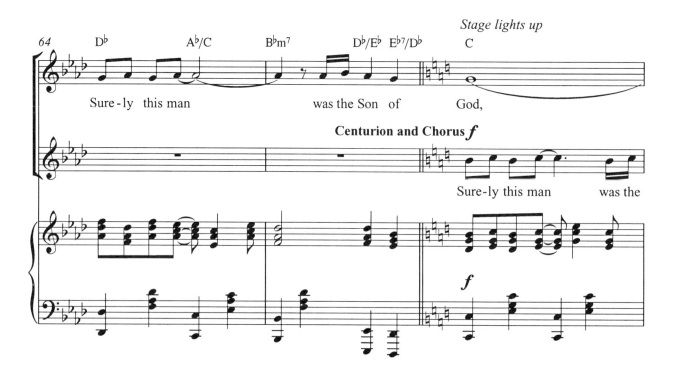

81

SCENE 8: JOSEPH OF ARIMATHEA AND NICODEMUS RETURNING FROM BURYING JESUS

Joseph of Arimathea and Nicodemus are walking along together.

Nicodemus	I'm still finding all this hard to take in, Joseph. Do you realise – we have just buried the Son of God. *(repeats, more deliberately)* We have just buried the Son of God. It just doesn't make sense. None of it makes any sense at all.
Joseph	But we've always known that whoever claims to be the Son of God must die – we've had that drummed into us since we were boys.
Nicodemus	Yes, I know . . . but now it's actually happened . . .
Joseph	Being torn between keeping up our image in the council – even when we disagreed with their verdict – and coming out in the open about believing him – that was the hard bit. You're either for him or against him. *(pause)* Do you think speaking up could have made a difference?
Nicodemus	If you mean could we have influenced the Sanhedrin – even Pilate failed there.
Joseph	Well, yes, but we failed him too. Worst of all, it's too late to do anything about it.
Nicodemus	At least we gave him a decent burial. Saved him being slung into a common pit. Good that you had your own tomb to use, Joseph.
Joseph	Mmm. Shame we had to do it so quickly.
Nicodemus	Oh, knowing women, some of them will go back and make a proper job of embalming.
Joseph	I'm sure they wouldn't wish to imply that your expensive spices weren't a gesture of your devotion to Jesus, too.
Nicodemus	Mmm . . . secret devotion. I only wish I'd spent more time with him. Proper time. *(pause)* Did I ever tell you – I went to him at night once, so no one would see me? We had this really extraordinary conversation.
Joseph	Extraordinary? In what way?
Nicodemus	Jesus said that no one could see the kingdom of heaven unless he was born again.
Joseph	Mmm, I see what you mean. Sounds like a physical impossiblity.
Nicodemus	Yes, that's just what I said. But of course, he wasn't meaning it in the physical sense. He said that a man must be born of water and the spirit if he is to enter the kingdom of heaven.
Joseph	How can that be?

Nicodemus	That's just what I said again. Then he said that if I'd had difficulty understanding when he talked about earthly things, how would I ever believe when he talked about heavenly ones.
Joseph	So . . . did you understand at all?
Nicodemus	Not really, not then. But now . . . now I do begin to see. 'For God so loved the world that he gave his only Son.' That's what he said. 'That whoever believes in him shall not perish but have eternal life.'
Joseph	That's quite a promise, isn't it?
Nicodemus	And he also said that even though light had come into the world – that was Jesus himself – men preferred darkness because it didn't show up their evil deeds. That was true, wasn't it? That's why his enemies hated him so much, because he exposed them for what they were.
Joseph	And of course, they were the very people he came to save.
Nicodemus	There are none so blind as those who will not see.
Joseph	None so deaf as those who will not hear.
Both	*(as they exit)* For God did not send his Son into the world to condemn the world, but to save the world through him.

SCENE 9: THE TWO MARYS ON THEIR WAY TO THE TOMB

LOVE DIVINE

Mary Magdalene stands alone on stage

Mary, mother of James, enters carrying spices

I saw it then – the look up-on his face – he'd gi-ven all he had to give. I saw a King stand-ing in my place, who went to die that I might

90

Mary, mother of James gives some spices to Mary Magdalene
and they exit together

SCENE 10: RESURRECTION MORNING – A ROADSIDE CELEBRATION

Disciples are wandering around looking dazed and perplexed. They are trying to come to terms with what has happened and are a bit 'scratchy' with each other.

Peter	*(pacing about)* So . . . what now? I mean . . . what now? What now?
Andrew	*(rather impatiently)* Stop pacing about saying 'What now?' Nothing – that's what. Although it would no doubt salve your conscience if Jesus were to . . . I don't know . . . suddenly appear, so you could apologise for disowning him.
Philip	Andrew, that's a bit harsh.
Peter	No, it's probably true. Although if that were to happen, Jesus would have every right to disown me. It wasn't as if I denied him to an interrogation committee. It was just a servant girl. Even more demeaning.
Matthew	Well, he's not likely to appear is he? He's buried in a tomb and all our hopes and dreams are buried with him.

Mary comes rushing in.

Mary	*(rather hysterical)* He's not there! He's not there!
Peter	What do you mean – he's not there, he's not there? Who's not where?
Mary	Jesus – he's not in the tomb!
Andrew	Mary's just being hysterical. Is she drunk or something? She's talking utter nonsense.
Mary	You have to believe me. He really isn't there. We went with our spices to the tomb but when we got there, the stone was rolled away.
John	That's impossible. Pilate issued special instructions to put a seal on the stone – and he sent someone to guard it. There's no way it could have been moved.
Mary	Well, it was. We went inside – and the body of Jesus had gone.
Peter	Come on, Mary; this is just female imagination gone wild.

Disciples nod in agreement.

John	We all saw him die, Mary. You don't come back from that.
Mary	God can do it.
Andrew	Sure, God can do it – but where was God at Calvary? If he wanted him alive, what in heaven was he playing at?
Mary	No, listen; there's more. Two angels suddenly appeared in clothes that gleamed like lightning.
Andrew	*(shaking his head in disbelief)* She's really lost it now.
Mary	They said: 'Why do you look for the living among the dead? He is not here – he has risen!' *(looking pleadingly at Peter)* Don't you remember what Jesus told you when he was still with you in Galilee? 'The son of man must be delivered into the hands of sinful men, be crucified and on the third day' *(she speaks very deliberately)* 'be raised again.' Can't you see? That's exactly what's happened.

Judas, son of James	Get a grip of yourself, Mary.
Peter	No, wait. I'm going to see for myself. Come on, John, you come with me.

They run off. Mary exits and disciples talk, some standing, some sitting on the ground, shrugging and looking generally disheartened.

Judas, son of James	Going back to Peter's question: what now? What of the future? I suppose we'll have to go back to our old jobs, won't we?
Philip	Ideally, I suppose we should carry on teaching, like Jesus did. It seems quite unthinkable that all he achieved should end, just like that.
Judas	But expecting crowds to follow us like they did him would be unthinkable in itself. I know we watched him heal the sick and drive out demons and feed five thousand people from one packed lunch, but assuming that we could do it ourselves . . . no, we haven't got the authority – we're just not qualified.

The disciples are quiet for a moment, each one looking deep in thought.

Matthew	I keep going over, in my mind, the things Jesus used to say to us. Were we so dim that we couldn't see they were all leading up to something?
Andrew	I tell you, they won't find anything. Mary's making it all up because she so much wants it to be true. You know what women are like.
Philip	Andrew – what is the matter with you? You're sounding as if you don't even care.
Andrew	*(impatiently)* Of course I care! *(puts one hand over his eyes, concealing his tears)* *(more gently)* I care just as much as the rest of you, but . . . I suppose I'm just too frightened to believe it . . . it would be such a great comfort . . . but then if it wasn't true . . .
James	I know what he means, Philip – he's just cross and it's all coming out wrong. It's true – if we build up our hopes, our despair will be even greater, and then we . . .
Peter	*(rushing back in with John, interrupts James' sentence)* Mary is right! Jesus' body *has* gone. There were strips of linen there and the cloth that was round his head was folded neatly. *(he senses the disbelief of the others as he looks round at them)* Well, if anyone had *stolen* his body, they wouldn't have bothered to fold it like that, would they?
Bartholomew	First Mary, now you. You're just trying to convince yourselves.
Peter	I need no convincing; I saw an empty tomb. It's you I'm trying to convince. I tell you – he has risen.
Mary	*(rushing in, very excited)* I have seen the Lord! I have seen the Lord! I was crying outside the tomb and I suddenly heard this voice say: 'Woman, why are you crying? Who are you looking for?' I assumed he was the gardener so I asked him to tell me where he had moved Jesus. *(she clenches her hands together and looks almost unable to speak)*
Matthew	*(excitedly)* Well . . . go on, what happened then?
Mary	This man . . . this . . . gardener, just said 'Mary'.

Simon	But how did he know your name?
Mary	Because it wasn't the gardener at all. It was Jesus. It was him. *(by now everyone is listening excitedly, wide-eyed with amazement)*
James	What did you do then, Mary?
Mary	Oh, I knelt down and cried out 'Rabboni!' and I touched his feet – just to make sure I wasn't dreaming. But he said, 'Don't hold on to me, for I have not yet returned to the Father. Instead go and tell the others that I am returning to my Father and your Father, to my God and your God.'
James, son of Alpheus	I remember him saying that now – 'I came from the Father and I am going back to him.'
James	Then it must have been him. *(with deliberation)* It really must have been him!
Mary	I tell you, it was. I have seen the Lord! He has risen!
All	He has risen! He's alive!

They hug each other as the whole company come onto stage during the introduction to the next song.

ALIVE!

Brightly

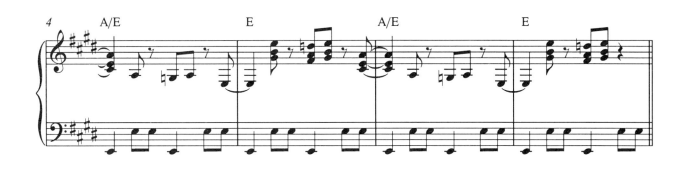

Chorus

A - live!   He is ri - sen, he's a - live!

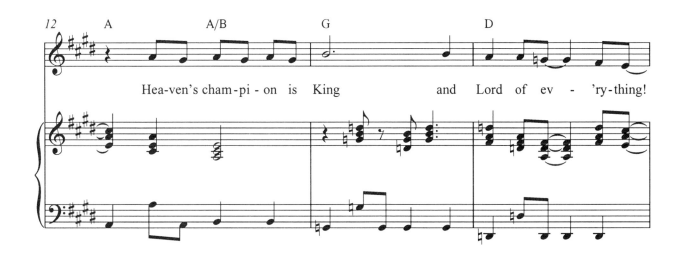

Hea-ven's cham-pi - on is King   and Lord of ev - 'ry-thing!

A - live! He is ri-sen, he's a-

live! He has turned the dark-est night to glo-ri-ous

light!

Je - sus has
We are the

con - quered hell, his peo - ple now to save, so
wit - nes - ses that Je - sus wants to use to

don't go look-ing for a bo-dy in an emp - ty grave.
spread the mes-sage of the re - sur - rec - tion news:

There's no more fear of death but
He has been raised to life in

98

IF YOU WANT TO FOLLOW JESUS

Nicodemus comes out of the crowd to centre stage
Everybody enters into the 'Calypso spirit'

Calypso
A
mf
Nicodemus
mf
D
E
If you want to fol-low Je - sus, to en-ter the king - dom of heav'n,
A
D
E
you got-ta do a Ni-co - de - mus, you got-ta be born a - gain.
A
D
You got - ta take off those shut - ters, so your
And it's ne - ver too late to en - ter, no, it's

eyes can see the truth.
ne-ver too late to say:
You got - ta take out those stop -
'I wan - na do a Ni - co - de -

- pers, so your ears can hear the good news. Oh,
- mus, I wan - na be born to - day!'

1.

D.S.

2.

Nicodemus and half of Chorus

Oh, if you want to fol-low Je - sus, to

en - ter the king - dom of heav'n, you got - ta do a Ni - co - de -

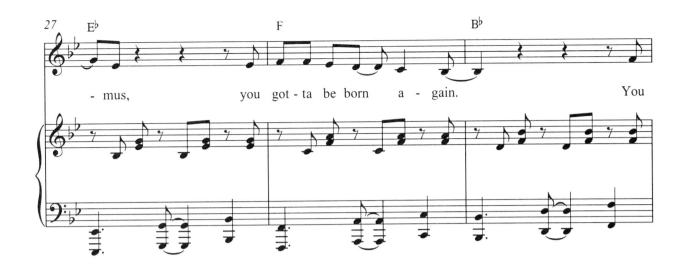

-mus, you got-ta be born a - gain. You

Peter and other half of Chorus

If you want to fol-low Je - sus, to en-ter the king - dom of heav'n,

got-ta take off those shut - ters, so your eyes can see the truth,

you got-ta do a Ni-co-de - mus, you

you got-ta take out those stop - pers, so your

104

TODAY I AM ALIVE TO TELL THE STORY (Reprise)

Lazarus comes bounding out of the crowd

Martha: *(over top of song introduction)* Oh no, he's going to sing that song again!

Everybody laughs and cheers

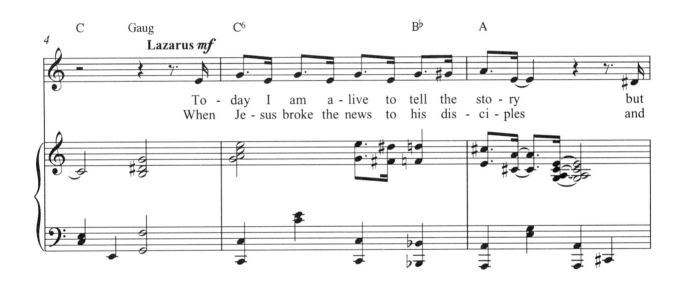

To - day I am a - live to tell the sto - ry but
When Je - sus broke the news to his dis - ci - ples and

if you could have seen me then, I real - ly looked so poor - ly, the
told them I had gone to sleep, they did - n't quite be - lieve it, they

And though they al - ways trust - ed Je - sus, the
peo - ple, still they said: 'Did - n't you know? He is al - rea - dy
dead.'

The vil - la - gers were look - ing out for
Je - sus came to find where I was

Je - sus. They saw him com - ing through our gate. They
ly - ing, it must have been quite plain to see; I

isn't dead –   let me han - dle this   my way.'
out   to   me: 'La - za - rus, come out of that cave!'

When

And though I was a - live   and kick - ing,   the

peo - ple, still   they said: 'La - za - rus,   go back to

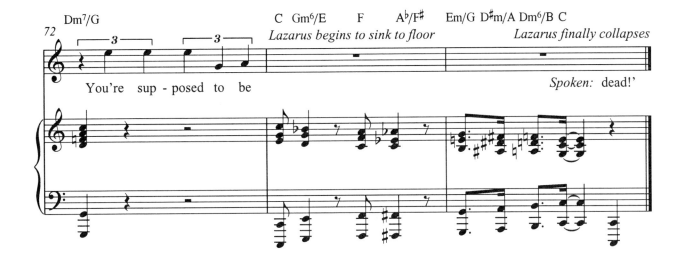

Lazarus   *(rising to his feet)* Well, that's the story, but it's not all of it . . . because the end
is up to you. Where do you stand in all this?

You see, the Chief Priests and Teachers of Law were so steeped in tradition
and rules and regulations that they became inflexible in their attitudes.
Could that be you?

Judas, even though he was a disciple of Jesus, betrayed him to his enemies.
He wasn't strong enough to stand up against Satan and allowed himself to be
taken over by his temptations. Could that be you?

Nicodemus was born in the same, physical way as the rest of us. But Jesus told him
he must be born spiritually as well. He had trouble understanding the Kingdom of
Heaven and how he could enter it. Could that be you?

Peter loved Jesus, but when the chips were down, when he feared his relationship
with him might jeopardise his own safety and popularity, he denied he ever
knew him. Could that be you?

The centurion went along with the stubborn requirements of his job without
making time to consider a change of lifestyle. Could that be you?

And Pilate: the lasting shame of Pilate will be that he gave in to opposition.
He chose the easy way out instead of sticking to his gut feelings.
Could that be you?

God so loved the world that he gave his only Son, that whoever believes in him
shall not perish but have eternal life. For God did not send his Son into the world
to condemn the world, but to save the world through him.

Jesus saved me from death and he will go on saving people – from spiritual death,
so that they will be alive – spiritually alive – to tell the story. To share with others
what they have seen and heard for themselves. And surely . . . this man, who did so
much good, who suffered so much injustice, who died on a cross for me, for you –
surely this man . . . *was* . . . the Son of God.

FINALE

Broadly

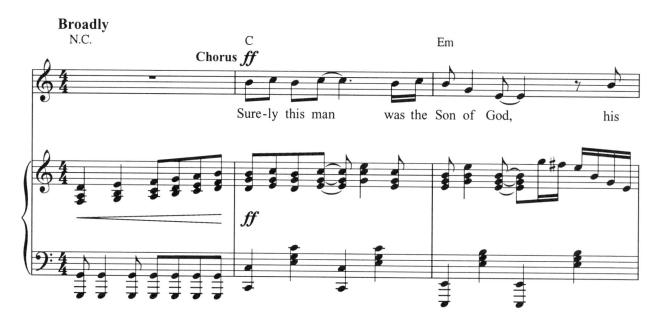

Sure-ly this man was the Son of God, his

on-ly Son, his cho-sen one, the right-eous one, the

ho-ly one. Sure-ly this man was the Son of

117

dise. There'll be no more cry - ing, there'll be no more pain; there'll be

no more suf - fer - ing or tears a - gain and the sov - 'reign Lord of

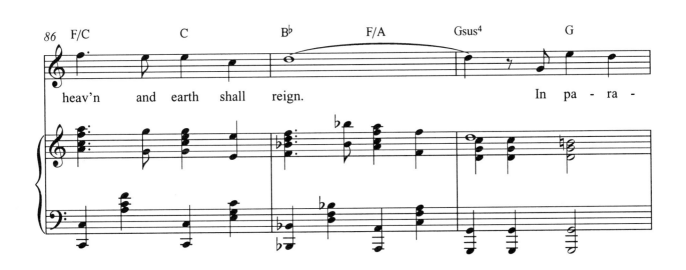

heav'n and earth shall reign. In pa - ra -

.

KEVIN MAYHEW PERFORMANCE LICENCE FORM

We are delighted that you are considering *Alive!...to tell the story* for production.
Please note that a performance licence is required and royalties are payable as follows:

10% of gross takings, plus VAT
(Minimum fee: £30.00 + VAT = £35.25)

This form should be returned to the Copyright Department at Kevin Mayhew Ltd. A copy, including our performance licence number, will be returned to you.

Name of Organisation _____

Contact name _____

Contact address _____

_____

Postcode _____

Contact Telephone No. _____   Contact Fax No. _____

E-mail _____

Date(s) of performance(s) _____

Venue _____

Seating capacity _____

Proposed ticket price _____

I undertake to submit performance fees due to Kevin Mayhew Ltd within 28 days of the last performance of *Alive!...to tell the story*, together with a statement of gross takings.

Signature _____

Name (please print) _____

On behalf of _____

Address if different from above _____

_____

To be completed by Kevin Mayhew Copyright Department:

Performance Licence No. _____ is issued to _____

for _____ performances of *Alive!...to tell the story* on _____

Copyright Department, Kevin Mayhew Ltd, Buxhall, Stowmarket, Suffolk, IP14 3BW
Telephone number: UK 01449 737978   International +44 1449 737978
Fax number: UK 01449 737834   International +44 1449 737834
E-mail: info@kevinmayhewltd.com

Also available by Susie Hare

A Special Kind of Present

1450188   1 84003 601 X

A Special Kind of Present is a musical drama aimed at children in Key Stages 1 and 2. It's packed with music that is catchy and some of the songs can be used all year round. It tells the story of four children who want a Christmas present that is special.

It's a fun-packed production which brilliantly contrasts the commercial side of Christmas with the real meaning of the Nativity. There are parts for six main characters plus unlimited others, with piano accompaniment.

Includes a FREE CD of all the songs.

Follow That Star

1450189   1 84003 600 1

Follow That Star is a jazz cantata aimed at children in the 10-16 age group. It tells the Christmas story from a new perspective, with lively, contemporary language and catchy, memorable tunes.

It has a lightly humorous easy style and keeps moving energetically from beginning to end. It is scored for soloists, a group of singers and whole choir, with piano accompaniment.

Duration approximately 40 minutes. Includes a FREE CD of all the songs.